Look What I Found!
¡Mira lo que encontré!

by Deborah Schecter

ISBN: 978-1-338-70273-6
Illustrated by Anne Kennedy
Copyright © 2020 by Deborah Schecter. All rights reserved.
Published by Scholastic Inc., 557 Broadway, New York, NY 10012

10 9 8 7 6   68   23 24 25 26/0

Printed in Jiaxing, China. First printing, June 2020.

Look what I found!
I found a stick.

¡Mira lo que encontré!
Encontré un palo.

I found a stone.

Encontré una piedra.

I found an acorn.

Encontré una bellota.

I found a pine cone.

Encontré una piña.

I found a leaf.

Encontré una hoja.

I found a feather.

Encontré una pluma.

I found six things all together!

¡Encontré seis cosas en total!